It's My Time

A Guided Journal to Deeper Self-Love

Delores C.S. James

BEN CHRIS GROUP

It's My Time: A Guided Journal to Deeper Self-Love

Copyright © 2020 Delores C.S. James

Published by Ben Chris Group

ISBN 978-1-7355919-0-2

BEN CHRIS GROUP

This Journal Belongs To:

www.keepittightsisters.com

self-love

noun

regard for one's own well-being and happiness (chiefly considered as a desirable rather than narcissistic characteristic)

• •

Hello Ladies! Are you ready to begin a new chapter in your self-love journey? Some of you are starting the self-love journey with shame, regrets, and disappointments, while others are humming to the rhythm of a freedom song. Wherever you are on the journey, the affirmations and prompts in this guided journal will help you make your health, happiness, and well-being a priority. So, take a few minutes each day to reflect, reconnect, and refresh your soul. Oh, and for the days you don't feel like writing, feel free to doodle or color on the pages. After all, it's your time!

• •

KEEP IT TIGHT SISTERS

EAT MOVE BREATHE

Introduction

Self-love does not come easy for everyone. In fact, I think that loving ourselves unconditionally is one of the hardest things we will ever do. And, self-love gets even more difficult in a society where it seems that we're all hustling and grinding at the expense of our mental and physical self.

Valuing and practicing self-love is important when you feel like you're not enough and can never have enough. Self-love is not a selfish "me first all of the time." Instead, it is more of "a healthy, whole me is my best gift to myself, family, and the world."

It's My Time is a guided journal that uses a creative approach to daily mindfulness and deeper self-love. Each motivational call to action is followed by a liberating quote, lined page to write your thoughts, and cathartic activity that affirms you at every step of making your health, happiness, and well-being a priority.

So, don't wait until you're stressed, burnout, and feeling unappreciated to practice-self-love. Use this guided journal as a mini-retreat from the daily hustle and grind. Start at the beginning or be radical and start in the middle.

Now, let's get started on that deeper self-love journey.

KEEP IT TIGHT SISTERS

START EACH DAY WITH GRATITUDE

EAT   MOVE   BREATHE

Gratitude: the quality of being thankful

List 4 things for which you are grateful.

KEEP IT TIGHT SISTERS

FEED YOUR SOUL DAILY

EAT   MOVE   BREATHE

Your soul is living and breathing and needs to be nourished

Color the mandala as you reflect on ways
to feed your soul this week.

KEEP IT TIGHT SISTERS

BE GENTLE
WITH
YOURSELF

EAT   MOVE   BREATHE

How can you be gentle
with yourself today?

KEEP IT TIGHT SISTERS

LEARN TO
WAIT WELL

EAT   MOVE   BREATHE

Wait: to stay where you are until a particular time or until something happens.

I am waiting for these things to happen:

KEEP IT TIGHT SISTERS

LAUGH OFTEN

EAT   MOVE   BREATHE

Laughter is medicine for the soul, so laugh often

KEEP IT TIGHT SISTERS

NEVER SACRIFICE YOURSELF

EAT   MOVE   BREATHE

Stop sacrificing your health, time, energy, and the essence of who you are.

I will stop sacrificing myself by:

KEEP IT TIGHT SISTERS

SPEAK YOUR TRUTH OFTEN

EAT   MOVE   BREATHE

Speaking your truth comes from knowing who you are and your purpose in life.

When was the last time you spoke your truth? What did you say? How did it make you feel?

KEEP IT TIGHT SISTERS

LEARN FROM YOUR MISTAKES

EAT   MOVE   BREATHE

What did you learn from your last big mistake? What would you do differently?

KEEP IT TIGHT SISTERS

CHOOSE
HAPPINESS

EAT   MOVE   BREATHE

DATE

How can you add more happiness to your life?

Color the mandala as you reflect on ideas.

KEEP IT TIGHT SISTERS

CHOOSE
PEACE

EAT   MOVE   BREATHE

Peace: freedom from dispute and dissension.

What is the biggest thing that is robbing you of peace?

KEEP IT TIGHT SISTERS

CHOOSE JOY

EAT   MOVE   BREATHE

DATE

"Joy lies in the fight, in the attempt, in the suffering involved, not in the victory itself." — Mahatma Gandhi

34

Write in the circle 3 things that bring you joy.

KEEP IT TIGHT SISTERS

CHOOSE LOVE

EAT   MOVE   BREATHE

DATE

_____

"A friend is someone
who knows all about
you and still loves you."
--Elbert Hubbard

Write the initials of 5 people who know all about you, yet still love you.

KEEP IT TIGHT SISTERS

OWN YOUR
QUEENDOM

EAT   MOVE   BREATHE

Claim or reclaim what is
rightfully yours

What are the characteristics of a good queen?

KEEP IT TIGHT SISTERS

YOU ARE
ENOUGH

EAT   MOVE   BREATHE

You are enough, no
more, no less

Write 4 positive statements about yourself

KEEP IT TIGHT SISTERS

YOU HAVE
ENOUGH

EAT   MOVE   BREATHE

You have enough to get
started, so take a step

Where do you want to go? What's your next move?

Write 4 baby steps that you need to make it happen.

SPEAK LIFE OVER YOUR DRY PLACES

EAT   MOVE   BREATHE

Speak life over your dry places and watch your tears bring them to life

The circle below represents water. Write 3 dry places in your life that need to come alive.

KEEP IT TIGHT SISTERS

ADVOCATE
FOR
YOURSELF

EAT   MOVE   BREATHE

Life is not fair, so be your own advocate

10 Steps to Being Your Own Advocate

1. Believe in yourself
2. Know your rights
3. Decide on what you want
4. Get the facts
5. Plan a strategy
6. Get support from your crew
7. Identify your target
8. Communicate clearly
9. Stay calm
10. Be firm and persistent

Adapted from wellness recovery action plan
www.mentalhealthrecovery.com

KEEP IT TIGHT SISTERS

STARE DOWN
FEAR

EAT   MOVE   BREATHE

Fear does not own you

WRITE 4 OF YOUR FEARS ON THE TAIL OF THE KITE.

Release your fears

"You gain strength, courage and confidence by every experience in which you really stop to look fear in the face. You are able to say to yourself, 'I have lived through this horror. I can take the next thing that comes along.' You must do the thing you think you cannot do."

ELEANOR ROOSEVELT

KEEP IT TIGHT SISTERS

KNOW YOUR
WORTH

EAT   MOVE   BREATHE

Know the difference
between what they're
offering and what you're
worth

Color the mandala as you think about how much you're worth.

KEEP IT TIGHT SISTERS

TREASURE SILENCE

EAT   MOVE   BREATHE

"Listen to silence. It has
so much to say."
--Rumi

On a scale of 1 to 5, how many stars do you give yourself for regularly practicing silence? Color the number of stars.

Silence recharges your mind
Silence gives space to think
Silence sparks creativity
Silence lowers stress
Silence grounds you
Silence calms you

KEEP IT TIGHT SISTERS

TREASURE
SOLITUDE

EAT   MOVE   BREATHE

Learn to enjoy your own company

"Blessed are those who do not fear solitude, who are not afraid of their own company, who are not always desperately looking for something to do, something to amuse themselves with, something to judge."

PAULO COELHO

KEEP IT TIGHT SISTERS

LET GO OF PERFECTION

EAT   MOVE   BREATHE

DATE

There is no perfection, only beautiful versions of brokenness

SHANNON L. ALDER

KEEP IT TIGHT SISTERS

GLOW FROM THE INSIDE

EAT MOVE BREATHE

*Let your inner beauty
and character shine
brightly*

Glow: a steady radiance of light.

In the mirror below, write 5 things about your character that shine brightly.

KEEP IT TIGHT SISTERS

BUY
YOURSELF
FLOWERS

EAT   MOVE   BREATHE

Buy a single rose or send
yourself a bouquet

Have fun coloring the flower.

KEEP IT TIGHT SISTERS

LEARN TO SAY "NO"

EAT   MOVE   BREATHE

Saying "no" might be the
most courageous thing
you do today

12 Polite and Not So Polite Ways of Saying "No"

1. Nope
2. Nah
3. No way
4. Not now
5. No thanks
6. Certainly not
7. Hell no
8. By no means
9. I already made plans
10. That doesn't fit my schedule
11. I am not a fool
12. I have other commitments

KEEP IT TIGHT SISTERS

SET
BOUNDARIES

EAT   MOVE   BREATHE

Lack of boundaries
invite lack of respect

Write 4 areas in your life where you need to set boundaries. Put the initial of a person who needs to respect your boundaries next to each one.

KEEP IT TIGHT SISTERS

UNPLUG AND RECHARGE

EAT   MOVE   BREATHE

"Come away and rest awhile." Mark 6:31

Describe your ideal vacation place

What types of activities would you do?

Great Ideas for a
Staycation at Home

1. Spa day alone or with friends
2. Visit local sights
3. Host a dessert party
4. Try a new restaurant
5. Take a day trip
6. Host a film festival at home
7. Lounge at the pool
8. See a performance
9. Go to a game
10. Try a new club or bar
11. Go to the beach
12. Go for a hike
13. Do a picnic in a park
14. Visit a nearby winery
15. Read some trashy novels

KEEP IT TIGHT SISTERS

MAKE SLEEP YOUR SUPERPOWER

EAT   MOVE   BREATHE

Make bedtime your
happy hour

On a scale of 1-5, how would you rate the overall quality of sleep that you get at night? _____

Write four things you can do to get better quality sleep?

Benefits of Sleep

Sleep regulates the hunger hormone
Sleep keeps your heart healthy
Sleep improves your memory
Sleep reduces inflammation
Sleep increases alertness
Sleep boosts immunity
Sleep reduces stress

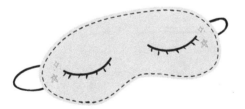

KEEP IT TIGHT SISTERS

EMBRACE MORNINGS

EAT   MOVE   BREATHE

Morning rituals set the
tone and declare your
intentions for the rest of
the day

10 Morning Rituals to Get Your Day Off to a Great Start

1. Don't snooze the alarm
2. Make your bed
3. Drink a glass of water
4. Open the blinds
5. Breathe deeply for 5 minutes
6. Read something inspirational
7. Pray, meditate
8. Write in a gratitude journal
9. Stretch for 10 minutes
10. Turn up the music

Rise and Grind!

KEEP IT TIGHT SISTERS

FORGIVE OFTEN

EAT   MOVE   BREATHE

Release yourself from
the prison of
unforgiveness

When was the last time you forgave someone? What did they do? How did it feel to forgive them? Write "forgiveness" in the circle.

Forgiveness is the fragrance that the violet sheds on the heel that has crushed it.

MARK TWAIN

KEEP IT TIGHT SISTERS

DO YOUR
BEST TODAY

EAT   MOVE   BREATHE

Do your best, no more, no less

Always do your best.
What you plant now
you will harvest later.

OG MANDINO

Color the mandala as you think about how you can do your best every today.

Today, I give myself
permission to fail while
doing my best.

Signed

_____

KEEP IT TIGHT SISTERS

DEFINE YOUR VISION

EAT   MOVE   BREATHE

Your vision helps to
define and manifest
your future

Your vision defines how you commit to living your life. It goes beyond the "stuff" you want to have by a certain age.

Your vision gets to the essence of: 1) who you want to be, 2) how you want to live your life, 3) what you want to be known for, 4) what you want to accomplish, and 5) what types of experiences you want to have.

MY VISION FOR THE NEXT 5 YEARS

I want to be known for . . .

I want to accomplish . . .

I want to have these experiences . . .

KEEP IT TIGHT SISTERS

DREAM BIG

EAT   MOVE   BREATHE

DATE

The future belongs to
those who dream big

Dreaming big gives you the mental freedom to pause and think about what you want out of life. It means having high standards so that you can stretch and grow.

Forget all of the reasons why you can't make your dreams a reality. DREAM BIG.

Describe one of your biggest dreams in the circle

KEEP IT TIGHT SISTERS

DREAM IN COLOR

EAT   MOVE   BREATHE

Dreaming in color
stimulates your emotions
and move you to action

Color the mandala as you reflect on ways to make your big dream happen.

KEEP IT TIGHT SISTERS

AIM FOR PROGRESS

EAT   MOVE   BREATHE

DATE

Forget perfection, and
aim for progress instead

113

Question: How do you eat an elephant?
Answer: One bite at a time.

Question: How do achieve your goal?
Answer: One step at a time.

DON'T STOP. YOU'RE MAKING PROGRESS!

KEEP IT TIGHT SISTERS

BUILD YOURSELF A TRIBE

EAT   MOVE   BREATHE

Having a tribe allows you to have other people in your life that want to love and nurture you, but you have to allow them to do so . . . We all need each other, often more than we are willing to admit, and we are all deserving of love. So go forth and build your tribe, because we all need each other.

WWW.THEEVERYGIRL.COM

List the names of 4 women who are (or can be) in your tribe, and describe the qualities that each one brings.

KEEP IT TIGHT SISTERS

CELEBRATE
SMALL WINS

EAT   MOVE   BREATHE

Celebrate your small
wins while you wait for
the big ones

Write 3 small wins that you had this week on the balloons.

KEEP IT TIGHT SISTERS

YOU'VE GOT THIS!

EAT   MOVE   BREATHE

Life is tough, but so are you. You've got this!

I wish you well on your self-love journey.

Join us at www.keepititightsisters.com where we help women to love their bodies, foster a nourishing relationship with food, and achieve their health and wellness goals.

Made in United States
Troutdale, OR
08/02/2023

11773967R00076